Peter Rabbit™
Animal Friends
Sticker Activity Book

FREDERICK WARNE

What's Missing?

What has Peter Rabbit lost in Mr. McGregor's garden? Look at the pictures below and find a sticker for the first letter of each one. When there is a sticker in each box, you will be able to read what Peter has lost!

What colour coat is Peter wearing? ....

Dotty Peter!

Mr McGregor is looking for naughty Peter!
Follow the numbers and join the dots to finish
the picture, then colour it in.

Happy Families Word Search

Peter Rabbit and Tom Kitten have lots of sisters! Find a sticker of each one, then see if you can spot all their names in the big square.

Peter

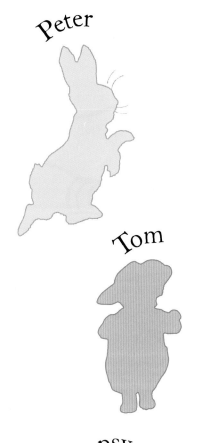

P	E	T	E	R	B	N	E	C
T	U	S	U	J	A	P	K	O
F	L	A	M	O	P	P	E	T
L	O	A	W	A	D	I	N	T
O	M	I	T	T	E	N	S	O
P	T	A	A	E	N	A	R	N
S	M	O	P	S	Y	P	I	T
Z	A	J	M	A	T	L	O	A
A	T	A	N	W	M	A	R	I
O	F	L	O	P	S	Y	A	L

Tom

Mopsy Cotton-tail

Flopsy

Mittens

Moppet

How many sisters does Peter have? ....

How many sisters does Tom have? ....

4

Fun with the Flopsy Bunnies

The Flopsy Bunnies are always getting into mischief! Today they are helping themselves to the lettuces in Mr. McGregor's garden. Colour in this picture of the Flopsy Bunnies using your favourite pencils or pens.

Can you count how many bunnies are eating lettuces?..............

Mrs. Tittlemouse's House

Mrs. Tittlemouse's house is full of sandy passageways which are often blocked by uninvited guests. Can you help her to the front door? Find a sticker for each visitor before you begin.

START

How many visitors are there altogether? ....

FINISH

Tom Thumb and Hunca Munca

Tom Thumb and Hunca Munca
are very disappointed to discover
the delicious looking ham is made
of nothing but plaster.
Find the missing sticker
and then colour the picture.

S
H
O
E
S

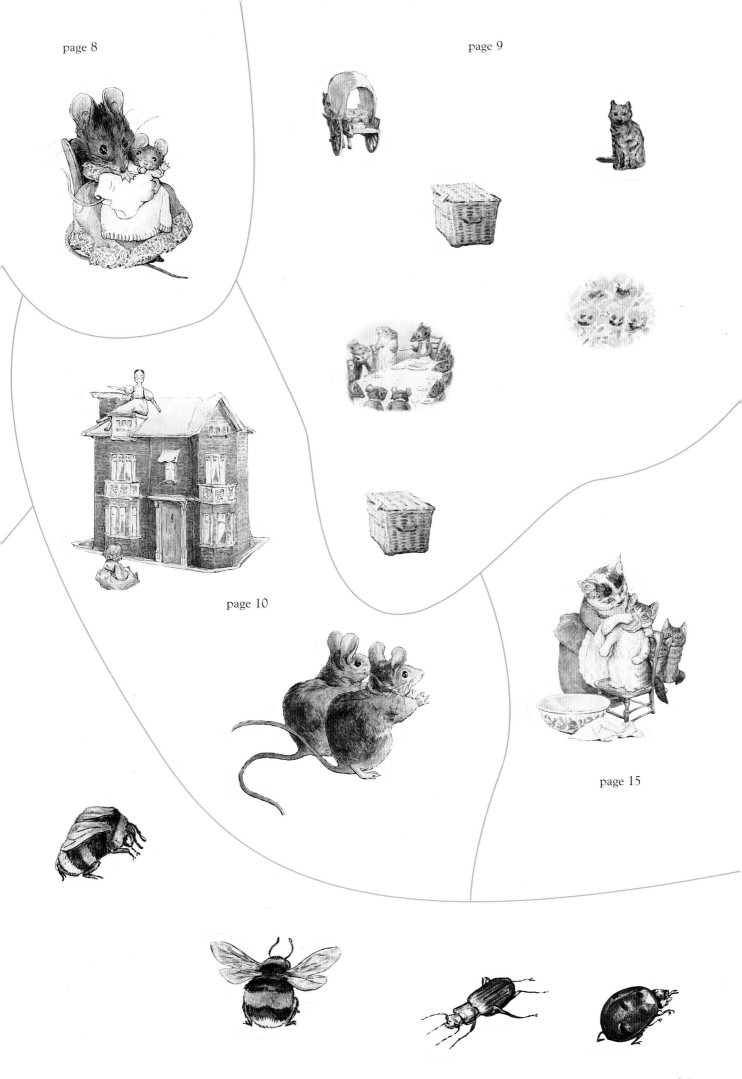

page 9

page 10

page 15

pages 6-7

A City Trip

Country mouse, Timmy Willie, has had quite an adventure. He has written a letter to his cousin telling her all about it. Some of the words are missing. Find a sticker for each word so you can read the letter too!

Dear Cousin,

Last week I paid a surprise visit to town.

I climbed into a big ____ and fell asleep.

When I woke up I was on a ____ being

taken to town! Once I got there, I ran into

the nearest hole. I found myself at

a party with lots of ____ .

I didn't like town. There was a fierce ____ .

So I got back in the ____ and was brought

home again. Here I can smell the ____ and

sleep in my own comfy bed.

I hope you are well.

Your cousin, Timmy Willie.

Doll's House Maze

Lucinda and Jane have gone for a drive, leaving Tom Thumb and Hunca Munca to have fun exploring the doll's house! Can you help them to find a way out before the two dolls return? Find the missing stickers before you start.

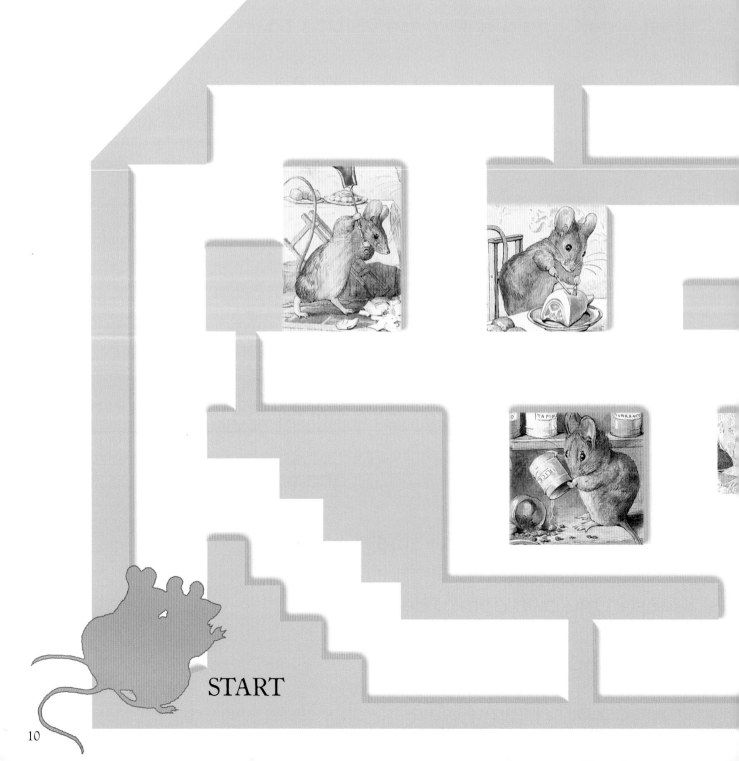

START

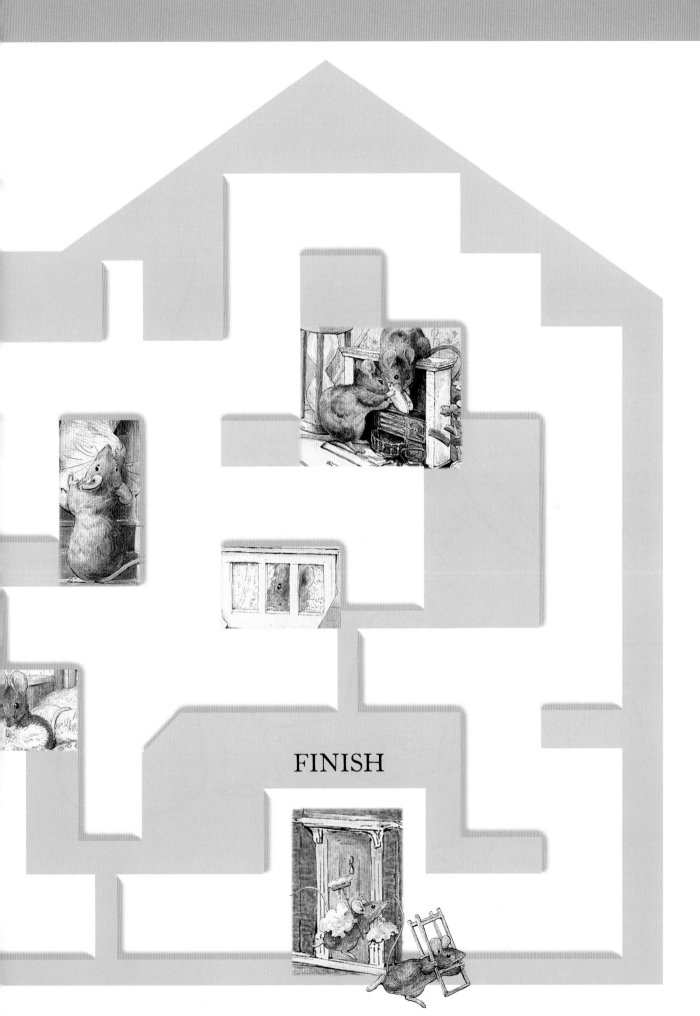

FINISH

Hungry Bunnies

Flopsy, Mopsy and Cotton-tail are eating bread and milk and blackberries. Delicious! Join the dots to finish the picture. You can colour it in afterwards.

Matching Pairs

Here are a set of pictures of Peter, Jemima and Benjamin. In each row there are two that are exactly alike. Can you see which they are?

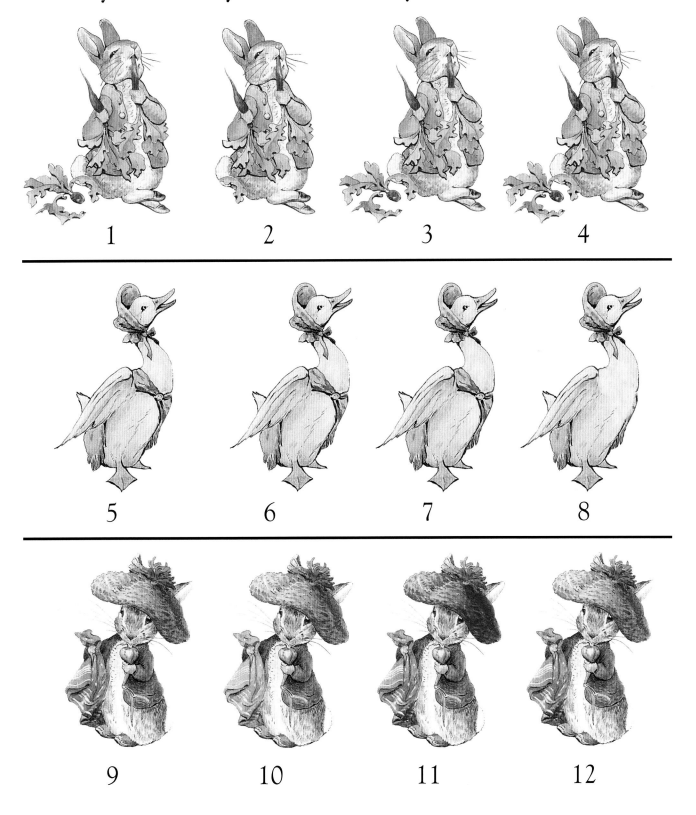

1 2 3 4

5 6 7 8

9 10 11 12

Bath Time

Poor Tom Kitten doesn't like baths! See if you can spot the 7 differences between these two pictures. Circle them as you find them.

Colour the Kittens

Find the sticker, then use your best pens to colour this picture of Tom Kitten and his sisters wearing their best clothes.

Answers

Page 2

What's Missing?
Peter has lost his SHOES.
Peter is wearing a BLUE coat.

Page 4

Happy Families Word Search

P	E	T	E	R	B	N	E	C
T	U	S	U	J	A	P	K	O
F	L	A	M	O	P	P	E	T
L	O	A	W	A	D	I	N	T
O	M	I	T	T	E	N	S	O
P	T	A	A	E	N	A	R	N
S	M	O	P	S	Y	P	I	T
Z	A	J	M	A	T	L	O	A
A	T	A	N	W	M	A	R	I
O	F	L	O	P	S	Y	A	L

Peter has 3 sisters;
Tom has 2 sisters.

Page 5

Fun with the Flopsy Bunnies
There are 7 bunnies.

Pages 6-7

Mrs. Tittlemouse's House
There are 9 visitors.

Pages 10-11

START

FINISH

Page 13

Matching Pairs
1 and 3
5 and 6
9 and 12

Page 14

Bath Time